How the Sailfish Got its Name

Written by
JT Jester

Illustrated by
Aaron & Michelle Grayum

How the Sailfish Got its Name

© 2022 JT "Jester" Mestdagh

Words and Story by JT "Jester" Mestdagh | jtmestdaghfoundation.org

Illustrations and Book Design by Aaron and Michelle Grayum
The Gray Umbrella, LLC | thegrayumbrella.com

First edition, 2022

Published by:
Elite Online Publishing
63 East 11400 South #230
Sandy, UT 84070
EliteOnlinePublishing.com

ISBN: 978-1-956642-27-8 (eBook)
ISBN: 978-1-956642-38-4 (Hardback)

JUV002170
JUV002100

This book is printed in the United States of America.

When your child reads JT Jester's new book, "How the Sailfish Got Its Name," he or she will not only enjoy a wonderful story about transformation and kindness, but you'll be helping children around the world with learning and physical differences by supporting the JT Mestdagh Foundation. The foundation strives to improve the lives of children with congenital colorectal issues and those with dyslexia and other learning disabilities by providing them with the best possible educational testing, mentoring, and tutoring, especially using the Tattum Reading program. A portion of the proceeds of this book will go to the JT Mestdagh Foundation.

JTMestdghFoundation.org

One foggy morning, a sailor headed out for a day at sea off the coast of Florida.

The fog began to rise and the sailor decided to put up his jib.

When the sailor tried
to put up his main sail,
the fierce wind ripped
it into the water.

The anxious sailor was sad because he lost his favorite sail.

It was gone in seconds.

A school of fish
swam by.

All of a sudden they
got caught up in the
beautiful sail.

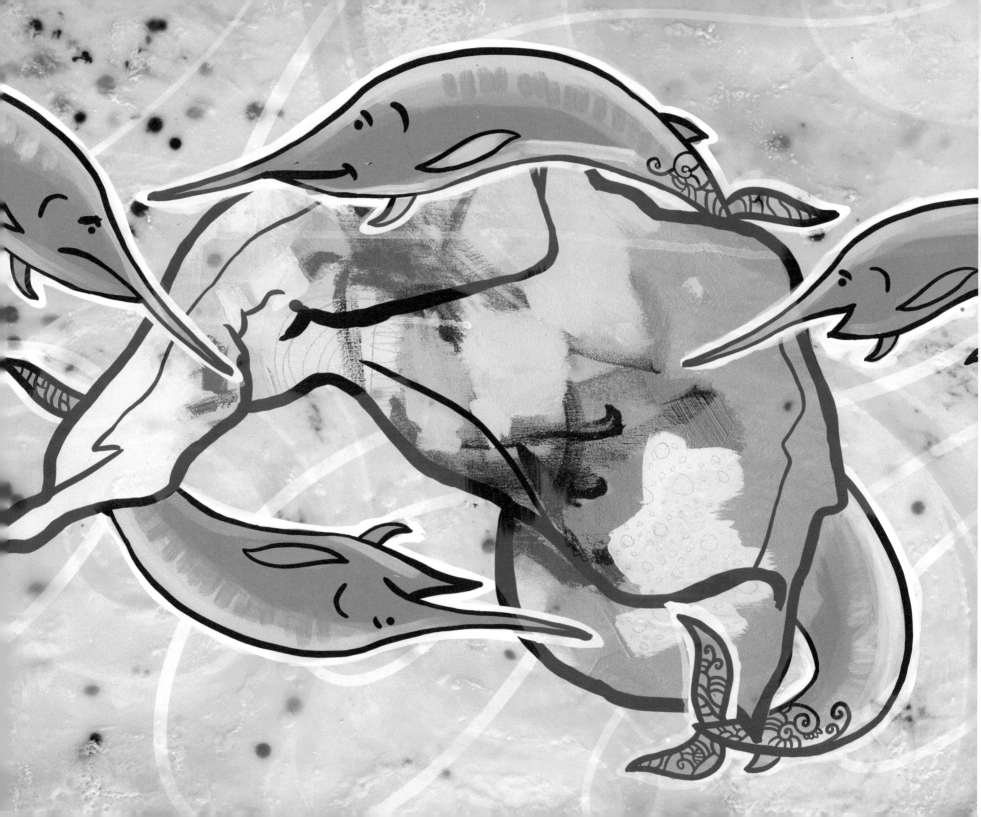

A barracuda heard
their calls for help.

The barracuda
used its razor blade teeth
to cut each fish out of the sail.

The fish were free.

The fish liked
the sail's
beautiful colors.

They tied pieces of the sail around
their backs
using jelly fish tentacles.

The fish loved the colorful sails
on their backs
because it made them
feel powerful.

They learned to use the sails to
swim better and faster
in the sea.

After time,
the colors started to blend,
becoming a vibrant blue.

From that day forward they
would be forever called
sailfish.

The End.

MISSION

By reaching up and reaching out, the JT Mestdagh Foundation sees a world changed and improved by children with congenital colorectal issues who receive world-class medical care, and by those with dyslexia and other learning disabilities who excel with the best possible educational testing, mentoring, and tutoring, especially using the Tattum Reading program. The Foundation also envisions these young people's families, caregivers, and educators surrounded with love and hope as well as practical tools and creative strategies to ease the demands that no one should face alone.

JT Mestdagh Foundation.org

JT Jester

Author. Speaker. Adventure Enthusiast!

"I want to share my story so people who feel alone and discouraged might feel well, less a lone, and more confident." - JT

y the time JT Jester was three years old, he had spent 250 days in the hospital, and he ndured sixteen major surgeries before he was sixteen. Diagnosed with VATER Syndrome, a rare ombination of several birth defects. JT's life was anything but easy. On top of his physical hallenges, he suffered dyslexia and short-term memory loss, which made learning nearly npossible for him. Yet JT pushed past his physical and educational roadblocks to achieving what any people told him he would never do... learn to read, graduate from high school, graduate rom college, and has now become a successful motivational speaker, influential podcast host, hilanthropist, and international bestselling author.

Follow JT at jtjesterspeaks

CPSIA information can be obtained
at www.ICGtesting.com
Printed in the USA
BVHW060328101122
650537BV00001B/4